Guitar!

SARAH TRIPP

CW00828337

Book Works

Guitar!

I have been wondering if, with the right listener, you could live with just two words.

I climb out from under you. Nay-nay, I am running
out of time to write this, you will be speaking soon.
I have maybe a month, maybe two. Naden-naden.
All your questions will need answering. And my
answers will lead to more questions. We are the only
ones left. Why stay? You bounced bue-bue-bues
around the Mithraeum. You halted, faced me –
you almost said it – then ran off into the shadows
ninging. Where is everyone? Ning-ning-ning.
Thinking, thinking – I've been thinking, these
stones are not inert, their mass keeps us cool. The
archaeologists and geologists quarry and leave.
The masons and the engineers break their tools.
It has not rained in your lifetime. You have not
seen a flower, yet you point them out in stories.
Nagen-nagen. What's the word? For people who

mend ropes. Boem, boem, bouem, baoume. Yes!
Balloon! Nah, nah, nah. I have the feeling you
understand everything. My conversation with the
stones goes on silently; you make them resonate
with echoes. Omus, omus, omus. The medic made
her excuses. She said, if you need me just ring the
bell – what bell? There is no bell. Nagen-nah!
You look at my feet and clap. We will walk home
when you are old enough to survive the journey.
Until then, I continue my conversation with the
– there's a storm coming over the horizon. Where
will it stop? On your nose? I try to stop you
climbing but you have impulses, I stand back. As
luck would have it you are handsome and funny.
Bal-al-al. Bumpity-bump! What was her name?
The last student to leave, her intensity made us pay
attention to the stones. Heather! You are missed.
The dome is complete. We dream of its mosaic.
Those tiles high, high up there, each one placed by
me. Bue! Yes! Blue! I tried hooking it out with my
little finger. Your lips closed tight over the blue tile.
Then your agitation set off our tears. The ladders
are too high to climb in this heat. When you start
talking we will not be able to forget these feelings.
The dry leaves jitter in the breeze. I work on after
our dinner. Some of the glazes are faulty, some of
the tiles crack, the odd word is broken. Cowardice
stops me returning. The oven is too hot. Our

windows open onto boards and poles: standards, ledgers, transoms wait. I wait. Once the sun sets I climb outside. Chukka-chukka, chukka-chukka, chukka-chukka booo! I dangle my legs over the edge, flexing my toes, one eye on you, one on the horizon's coral hue. Yes! Baa-baa! Well done! We have no roof, a myriad of workers rested here but not one roofer. No women, except for the archaeologist. The scaffolders were funny. So, the moral of the story is… And the scaffolder's moral was lost under clanging transoms. I cannot hold you up at the window any longer. Ing! Ing! Ing! Details have been removed; the Mithraeum is restored to a new, graphic glory. Once I get out from under you there is no way back.

I can just see 6 and a dot. The silhouette of a
domed lid is obscuring the minutes so I do not
know if I am nearer 6 or 7 a.m. From what I can
remember there is a gift box with a black silky
lining, a bubble wand in its green plastic sheath, an
empty instant coffee tin, a chocolate box composed
of two cylinders which slide in and out of each
other effortlessly and a jar with a domed lid, but
it is too dark to know. Oh, now I can see 7 and a
dot. I am wide awake, Vivian is sleeping. He sleeps,
I write. He never sees me write, or sleep for that
matter. If he is excited I write nothing. He has been
up for three hours, fighting sleep, fighting himself,
playing listlessly, too tired to go on, too tired to give
up. Outside, a thin fall of snow is hardening onto
the pavement. Without my tiny reading light it is

even darker. I was trying to find a sentence about loneliness and the edge of the city, in a book I have which is out of print. I don't know why he wakes up in the night to play. Something was missing, we looked for the yellow marble for a long time, then found the blue one. I am learning how to speak to him. This is not a question of words but of love. Guitar! means, Hello! Guitar? means, Will a guitar turn up in this story?

Here and now in the middle of the night, there is nobody I want to talk to, no one. I only want to hear myself, I only want to make my own noise. That is pretty much where I got to today; I tidied this room, I laid down on the carpet, I asked what I wanted, all I wanted was to make my own noise. I cannot imagine exhausting my hunger for noise. I am frightened of frightening you with my noise. It is too cold to write, my ankles are dangling, exposed below the hem of my dressing gown. I am starting to feel drowsy, or maybe just in need of warmth. I don't want to talk – I want to talk, makes no sense. Too cold to talk now. Nite.

It is 7.56 p.m. That is where I got to yesterday: 'noise', then I realised it was quite predictable and not even nearly right.

It is 8.32 a.m. How cold is it outside? Frost covers the upper branches of the tree. Oh, it's snowing, just as I was wondering. I can't tell you how to do this, I just know people *do* do it. They gain nothing from practice except experience, which has no value I can put into words. Already high on the swing, Vivian demanded, More! Isobel, who was drawing herself up into her jacket against the cold, grimaced and replied, More is happening! People lose, lose their money, lose their time (if time can be depleted) and lose their friends because, in the end, only you will care. I thought to myself, whatever is going on is my reality and I would rather make my own, with my own, in my own time with what I have to hand no matter how difficult. So, what do you do? You begin by choosing

Just Vivian stirring.

You begin by choosing someone.

It is very late. Or it is very early. More! means more. More! doesn't always mean more. More *is* smiling.

It is 12.29 a.m. The upturned hull of a boat is a Guitar! A wooden clock, shaped like a teardrop, on the wall above the cashier in the post office is a Guitar! Not rarely but often your practice will yield an experience which really can't be placed anywhere. It's not personal, nor social, nor cultural but something in between. Aman gains nothing. Chloe gains nothing. If anything this practice empties you out. It is a complex word, gui-tar, quite a difficult first word, as is ba-lloon, although all we say is Ba!

Exactly 12.29 again! But p.m. The winter sun is burning out the view from the window. Playgroup was astounding! Multistorey carpark and mini-kitchen were teeming with unspoken negotiations. I gain nothing, you gain nothing, if this accomplishes anything, it is a reverse movement. Like backwards walking, bumping into things hidden from you, finding the floor is actually uneven, pronouncing steps with your heels and backing away from what you can see. A strain is gained, confusion over something never normally noticed. I mean, I can't see everywhere inside and I can see everywhere outside, so, yes I think there may be more to the inside of the guitar than I know.

Perhaps undesirable.

It is 3.04 a.m. I had given up looking for my eyedrops before I sat down and here they are! I am really enjoying that tingly explosion followed by the salty drip a sneeze leaves in the back of your throat. The cold is now exiting rather than entering me. I am certain Vivian said, Me. Perhaps I say, Me, more than I realise. All backpacks are guitars, a boxy handbag with a buckle is a guitar, the saddlebag on a horse is a guitar, as is the saddle which, now I look with care, is guitar shaped. Guitar! originally refers to the second-hand ukulele lying on the carpet of his room. And after that the expensive acoustic guitar in the hard, black guitar-shaped case in the big bedroom; and the heavy bass guitar under the bed which is both giving and taking scratches as we drag it out across the floorboards daily; and the red electric guitar in the soft case which unzips along one side in a big, flowing 'S'. A case that can contain a guitar is called Guitar! and a case that cannot is called Guitar! Violins and harps are Guitars! Everyone dancing and singing is Guitar! A ripe pear with cheese is Guitar!

Guitar! means, Hello guitar!
Guitar! means, I love you guitar!
Guitar! means, More guitar!
Guitar! means, More!

Guitar? means, Do you like guitar?
Guitar? means, Can you play guitar?
Guitar? means, Will a guitar turn up in this story?
Guitar? means, Where is my guitar?

Guitar! is here, here and here. Every*here.*
Here, on the carpet in your room. Small. Blue.
Strings. And a mouth. Me guitar. Me! Upside down.
Balancing. On a corner. Of the mattress. Yoga!
Here, in a box. Push-flick-drop the clips. Soft, red,
bed for wood, strings and a Spanish mouth. Ouch!
if the lid falls. Strum slowly, shy fish, fly fish, bye fish.
Here, in the big bedroom. Rumbles. Up through our
knees. Can you feel? Bass. Bass guitar. Twang-wang-
wang. No strings, wires!
Here, unzips in a curve. Pinch the pull. Now pull!
Okay, we pull together. Red and white. Quiet pings.
Where are they? Not inside. No hole. Electric!

A saxophone case is a Guitar!
And the saxophone inside is a Guitar!
A satchel is a Guitar!
A purse is a Guitar!

A Guitar! swings from her shoulder.
A wheely suitcase is a Guitar!
A deep pocket is a Guitar!
A cardboard box is a Guitar!
Half a guitar nesting on a sofa, half in a photograph
of a room advertising something, on the side of a
van parked opposite us, while we wait for green at
the lights is Guitar!

The pattern around a guitar's soundhole is a Guitar!
A Ferris wheel is a Guitar!
The faceted iris of an owl's eye is a Guitar!
A bicycle wheel is a Guitar!
All those shapes which are circular but have no
hint of a sphere are Guitars! Not dots (which have
density) but all the spirals which repeat and turn
into whorls in the pattern on the carpet in the
library are Guitars!

A bench in the park is a Guitar!
A tree, a stump, a trunk, a branch, a bud are Guitars!
The wooden horse in his hand is a Guitar!
A broom handle is a Guitar!
A brush is a Guitar!
Any tool is a Guitar!
Today, women lifting weights in the gym were,
Guitar!

It is 9.26 p.m. Once he quietens there is a period of twitching where his limbs gradually forget what they were doing before he fell asleep. Eventually, they sleep too and I very, very gently lay him down, carefully disarming him. I say to myself, The lives of the townsfolk depend on you. There are no townsfolk except inside me, where their happiness does depend on a little more sleep.

She is standing outside a soundproofed room imagining what it is like inside. All she can see through the small glass window is a microphone and a dark space beyond where the person who speaks can stand or sit or – she walks round the side of the booth and peers in. There is a tall stool on which to perch. The room is shallow, excluding anything other than standing alone and speaking. The door is astounding, a foot deep and so heavy that when she pushes nothing happens. She shifts her weight forwards and has another go. The door pivots smoothly, soundlessly, miraculously! Then stops. She likes this door. Five minutes ago, maybe she would have left, but now, this door affirms her ambition. Behind this door she can make her noise.

Be busy, make the same mistakes everybody makes. You are too confused to go on. Once more then no more. You do, do and do again. Oh, once more. Then this happens. A surprising uprising out of tiredness, a felt direction, you want to go forwards, there is nothing to go to, there is nothing to it, this is suddenly easy.

I have purchased a self-illuminating pen so I can write in the dark. Stay off the wish. Do not try.

It is 3.02 a.m. One thing this pen allows me to do is to roll over, write down the thought which prevents me sleeping, then fall asleep. To put the thought down. This putting things down means I can forget about them. Nite! And I can do this silently because the tapping of a keyboard echoes in the dark house and wakes Vivian. There is a click. The click clicks the light on and off but muffling the pen under my pillow hides the click, from my ears at least.

But what turns out to be astonishing is the way this pen illuminates one word at a time. This pool of light is only big enough to illuminate 'illuminate'. So I only see the word I am writing. Not the word gone. Not the word past. The here-and-now word. Here, under this intense dot of light, each word unwinds, a gentle halo catching the dither of my hand. Very little reflection is going on with this one-word-at-a-time. The full stops are something else entirely. And hesitation is an empty spotlight. Here, beneath this nib, is some place new. And it feels like the words can go anywhere. Anywhere they like. And as they go, I feel lighter.

This new place appears only at the moment of pointing the nib, only in the position of about-to-write. Because I do not point until the word is tumbling out. Until its self-importance wakes me. Until it won't let me be. Until, rolling over, feeling for the self-illuminating pen, I put down the words, empty my hands, and fall asleep. You've got an honest face when you're sleeping.

And this is what I wanted to tell you, I cannot read what I wrote. I can go back one word at a time but I am always burrowing onwards, or backwards along the same tunnel. The other thing that disappears is the rest of my body. It is mainly my writing hand which exists, a creature extending beyond the hem of my sleeve, exposed and bleary.

It is 3.43 a.m. We have coughs, perhaps the same cough, perhaps not. I slept well then the following night NEW DROPLETS! catching in my throat. Vivian said, *My* guitar! Sometimes I face north, lying in bed with the electric blanket on, sometimes I face south overlooking the garden downstairs. My ears are blocked, I hear less but see more, more movement. I would like my car back. I sold it but now I would like to enjoy the knowing. Knowing the geometry of parallel parking, knowing the roads, just knowing how to get somewhere. And dig! Dig up the garden downstairs and plant vegetables. It is almost time to rebuild, sticking and securing the flaps will not do. After this, this enclosure, I will not go back outside in the same way. I will not walk as I did. I am not there any longer, I am every*here*. I am not going to speak as I spoke, work as I worked. No work here, no leisure either. I am learning so much. How to be shocked and bored. I had it all wrong. I just found a needle, on the floor, about to be under my foot!

The floor of the booth is carpeted. At her feet is a plug socket, a cable travels up to a reading lamp, she switches it on and climbs onto the stool. She discovers a handle in a handle-shaped rebate and guides the door slowly towards her – probably better not to shut yourself in. Enough, she thinks then hops down, walks back through the darkened house and climbs under the duvet.

It is 12.21 a.m. The cold has collapsed my will. I keep thinking of Lesley, then of Aman, then of Simon or Chloe. I keep placing them in their offices, their studios, their cars and rooms. Karen too, in her bed, reading. Peta swimming. The coins, chick-chick, black crunch, skittles, the bees, wheels off and wheels on, stickers, neigh-neighs, guitars, music time, Barnaby hiding, cushions on the floor, drawing, painting, bee wings, Tony Tuh Tur Tle.

The door closes tightly. She sits there. She sits there and looks back outside to where she was standing. Is the noise she wants to make for in here or out there? She looks down at the mic. Is this noise for you? The mic's black nub blanks her behind the pop-screen. She doesn't want to see out so she heaves the door open again and switches off the lights in the outer room then climbs back into the booth. YOU ARE AUTONOMOUS, you can say it out loud – no you really are free – but feeling free enough to use, or even see, the space up in front of you needs to accrete within a relationship, the words in your head are not enough. Someone needs to remind you in sparkling terms, to urge you to remember. Remember! Maybe she can say that to begin with. She says to the nub, YOU ARE AUTONOMOUS! Well that seems to be very much for outside this room, for someone real to hear but it, the statement, is something of a failure of words. Forget it, she will just be silent. BE SILENT. Nope, does nothing, means nothing. Remember! YOU ARE! HELLO! BYE BYE! Figure the rest out for yourself. Nite!

It is 4.46 a.m. How about this, you are NOT autonomous – well you are except there are so many things over the last ten years that have gone out of fashion in your mind, things you have done out of affection for people, to make your own feelings into gestures, parts of you becoming real when issued for another. What kind of noise is this? Not a good one, perhaps a metronome.

Nina parps Guitar!

Reversing beeps from the street below are a Guitar!
The clang and thud of a wet boot rolling off the
radiator is a Guitar!

A fork pranging against the kitchen floor is a Guitar!

Coins poured out from a jar are a Guitar!

Beads in a tub are a Guitar!

A sieve tapping the ceramic rim of a mixing bowl is
a Guitar!

One leg, not definitely attached, creaking when I
lean on the table to reach for anything slightly out
of reach is a Guitar!

Guitar! means, Come here!

It is 3.36 a.m. So what will this noise be like?
Not a huff. Perhaps a hum or a tup–pup–pup–pup.
A high-pitched clang, some huge problem dropped.

Why even record the noise? Why is she in the
booth? Some kind of fear of the total noise, its sweep
and reach. The silence of the booth is a solo. The
inverse that keeps everything in balance, making life
porous to my intentions again. I am over halfway
there now, I have the right kind of silence, the right
kind of enclosure, exclosure! This is what I have
learned, How to exclose yourself? How to *whisper*
whisper. There is a clock soundlessly ticking outside
the booth. I haven't worn my wrist watch in two
years. No good, I suppose, comparing.

She has been feeling queasy and sorrowful,
the effort to achieve small ambitions seems
overwhelmingly too much. She cannot find the
energy for complex plans. Then the Guitar! came
along to remind her that no effort needs be found
if you go in an unheard direction.

It is 5.15 a.m. and I realise there is no way to talk
of myself in the vocabulary I have. I want you
to know I am thin, flat, tired. I is combing my
happiness, the locks are falling around my shoulders,
more and more, forever, liberal, happening. I am
tired and hungry and high, like a vinegar sigh. Do
not consume alcohol. Please yourself. Guitar! means,
I am a Guitar! In life the wheels come off every
time, all of the time.

A red circle is a Ba!
Red dots on a spotted handkerchief are Ba!
A small, domed, red light on the robot's chest is
a Ba!
The red button illuminated on the remote control is
a Ba!
White polka dots floating out of a garden on a
blue balloon escaping over the hedge, on a gust of
wind dashing out, suddenly dancing over stripes on
the zebra crossing, wide-eyed, then lurching back
towards us into oncoming traffic. The dots, the
balloon, the bang as yet unheard, are Ba!

Ba! means, balloon.
Ba! means, BANG!

Three metallic pink stars, tethered by pink ribbon,
to a pink bench, outside the manicurists are Ba!

It is 2.43 p.m. Blue skies today with smudgy clouds. Let's go on holiday! The sky says something like that. My voice is returning but I sound different because my ears are still blocked. When the woman in the park asked if I felt better I apologised for my deep voice, but then an empty moment walked between us in which I realised I had either misheard her, or I sounded fine but I was not hearing myself correctly, or what her question wanted was a yes or a no and it didn't matter to her what my voice sounded like, or she was distracted by her own other interests or ailments, which I knew nothing of because I had not bothered to ask, disappointing our reciprocity. I am not entirely sure where I live. I thought all the doors on my street were keeping people whole, protecting them from their work, and the cold and the rain, but now I realise doors keep them safe from terror and worse. The doors are precious to me now, sacred, and I know they must remain intact.

She guides the door back and forth on its hinges. She finds a handle in a rebate on the inside. She finds a plug socket and switches on a reading lamp. She leaves the door ajar and climbs into the old air. But as she lifts her hip high enough to swing onto the stool, she remembers perching the last time she sat at a bar, which became an ache in her lower back as the evening dragged on. She had wanted to kick the bar stool out from under him, he was so serious. She slides back off and swaps the stool for a plastic chair but the legs poke out the door, which must be the reason for the thin stool. Best not to shut yourself in when you are alone. Enough, she walks back through the darkened house.

It is 7.23 p.m. Vivian fell asleep an hour early. I feel inanimate. The energy I would have spent reading stories, nursing, cradling, rocking, lowering, softly treading is wondering how it will get spent now. I can see the street outside clearly, my eyes are actually sharper with this surfeit of energy. Beautiful hot-red brake lights flare as each car decides which way on the crest of the hill. Should I share this windfall? When I used to go on a night out I did not drink alcohol. When he sleeps through what will I do with all the energy? I could do a lot. *Really* a lot. Could be amazing how much I will see. A bit frightening too. She walks back through the darkened house. Nite.

It is 12.13 p.m. The flight of a bird demands a
soaring sound. Especially against an opaque sky.
Some sound needs to be made as it cuts across my
view. Turn up the volume of a bird, turn down
the volume of, I am just fed up of certain sounds.
What kind of tool will I use to make this noise?
Scythe, flint, melon? There is no tool to make
noise, only a happenstance wrong wielding of an
awkward implement. I hear noises but they are
mainly alarming. Take me to a sound that grows
bolts and leaves and lanterns. It must be this silence
of his sleeping that houses something I have yet to
hear. Guitar! means joy if there is no guitar in the
room, and there is nobody around who can play the
guitar, and there is nobody to ask, and if it is not a
Thursday (when we listen to Gaynor), and when
the inflection of a question is absent, but when the
day is lovely, flowing then, unsurprisingly, we or I
or Vivian wants to exclaim, Guitar!

Guitar? means, When is Daddy coming home?
Guitar? means, Who will play guitar with Vivian?
Noona plays? With her – erm – head. Rabbits play?
With what? Ears. And tails. Rabbit jam.
Or Nique? Plucking with her claws. Tiberon?
Which? Bebe. Good. Bebe's tail can pluck. Fins can
strum. Uh-oh Bebe! Bebe has fallen in the guitar.
Hold on. Not the thumb, too short. Index and
middle, fingers like scissors in the mouth. If. I. Can.
Just. Sweep Bebe into the light. Now. Lift her.
Tah-dah! Bebe!
Bees are buzzing in the guitar-tree. Blue Bee, Yellow
Bee, Green Bee. Sometimes Purple Bee. Oops!
She bounced. And. Twang! Crack! Ouch! More?
Twang! Crack! Ouch! More?
Guitar! means, Spark! I have an idea! This propeller
with this guitar. Let's go. Now! To the guitar. Come
quickly! Take submarine to meet guitar, something
will happen.
Guitar! means, Let go! Vivian does it. Vivian plays
propeller.

Guitar! means, I hear singing!
Guitar! means, More singing!
Guitar! means, And dancing!
Gaynor on Thursday mornings is Guitar!
Her ukulele is a Guitar! Her bells and tambourines
are Guitar! Thursday is a nest of guitars.
Guitar! can be so many occasions, the occasion is
a nest, I have to work out what kind of nest this
Guitar! is?
More and more rolling around on the bed suddenly
becomes, Guitar!
Guitar! means, Yes!
Guitar! means, Stop!
Guitar! is exciting.
Sometimes, Guitar! doesn't mean anything.
Guitar! is the place, nestled on our sofa, between
two cushions, beside the window, here Isobel rested
our guitar. Where is she?

It is 1.02 p.m. My son is making me happy. *Guitar!*
Guitar! means, Can I take my guitar out with me
today? Who would you like to hear singing in
the library? Shall we go now? Would you like to
take someone in the backpack? He hopes to take
the guitar to singing, for singing and guitar to be
together. Guitar inside a circle of voices. His choice
is perfect. I do not know why I did not pack the
guitar. Fear of someone getting hit on the head or
poked in the eye. There it goes again, outside the
window, the magpie. There are ten months left of
the year. Bumble bees live underground. Honey
bees live high up in a hive. Wasps chew paper or
something. Where is Lesley? Is she at her desk or
walking Frank? I don't know.

Giddy, yellow, wheeze in my chest. Hayfever and
sunshine overpower me. Yes and no, the feeling is
very nearly better than love. And that worm, still
entire and determined burrows down, not frowning
at the compact mud. Yawning never, draped over
my finger, just throwing off esses in the air. She
moves the bottle bank then off she goes. Why? I
like being with you Vivian. I have nothing to say
but I want my words to reach you. What are you
doing Heather? Are you awake Chloe? Thank you
for writing. Did we rise early or did we rise in the
middle of the night? Do not rise at all. Pay attention
to what you do not want to say. Don't let yourself

get cold. It is good to sit down with you so many
months later and gently tap out something like,
We agree! Eat moderately. Fly over the distance,
pass, lob, chuck, fling yourself across. I can now eat
an apple, brush my teeth, open a window and the
noise does not wake him.

It is 11.36 a.m. Lesley is in Japan. It has stopped
raining. There are buds on the branches outside
the window. The sound of the branches is missing.
The sound of the buds is missing. I have lived here
twenty-six years. Without notice the birds start
singing. It is cold in the house. I call it home.
The wind swishes as it corners the side of the flat.
The tapering ends of the smallest branches tap
against the window. I didn't do so well this morning.
I got us where we were going but lost myself in the
exertion, and lost my connection with Vivian too.

It is 12.27 p.m. What is Japan? Lesley sent a postcard.
The central heating has woken up at the wrong
time. The trees are moving back to front through
the mirror on the wall. Will Simon move away?
The chimney vent on the tenement behind us is
spinning in reverse as the wind gets up. I haven't
known how to value the good feelings I have had
about people I do not know well. Why? In the
library, Louis was

A tomato is a Ba!
An egg is a Ba!
A light bulb is a Ba!
A spherical, paper lampshade hanging from the
ceiling is a Ba! If you want to touch the Ba! go up
high. If you want to touch the Ba! go up high. If
you want to touch the Ba! go up high, go up high.
If you want to touch

A round stomach (pregnant maybe) is a Ba!
A red pepper is a Ba! We cut the Ba! open and
inside is another tiny Ba! Ba! has inner and outer.
The outside is tense and taut, its shape evidence of
an inside. Something about the stalk is particularly
Ba! Here the air goes in, but not out, here the
inflation happens. Stalk is the Ba!'s origin.

Ba! means, BANG!

We have made several attempts to commit banged
Bas to rest. Ceremonies in boxes before bins. Saving
their knots on the summit of our fridge. Oh dear!
Poor Ba! Alfonso, the purple Ba, commemorated
in felt-tip and stuck on a stick, is a small artefact, a
confusion to be discussed, a conversation going all
the way back to the storm and the Ba! lost in the
street below our window, it seems as though the
shock will never be food.

Ba! live. Or expire.

Any flattened or flattening sphere, anything with
the capacity to hold nothing, to be punctured, to
have volume, to collapse (perhaps unexpectedly),
to be light, possibly almost weightless, to be found
suddenly flat, expended or underfoot, to come to
an unexpected end, to contain sadness, and to mean
loss, and therefore the possibility of more loss, to
have fragility and no more time and the drama of a
sudden remove. Ba! carries a possible BANG! The
streets are littered with Ba! All kinds of unexpected
endings met on the road, beneath a car, by accident,
a terrible map of Ba! across this city.

A bubble travelling a meniscus of apple juice is a Ba!

It is 12.35 p.m. The silence is amplified by the cold air gathered beside the window. I can have this silence, more of a stillness, within this room, the branches looking in, for an hour or two. And this stillness I have is *a* value. Is valuable. Wrong word. Is owned. I can have the stillness and remember to go and find it, to stop and take it again just by writing it down. Putting it down. Laying it down gently.

The booth has three glazed vacuums. Are you okay Chloe? Teaching. Learning how to teach. I hope you are not trying to make your lectures perfect. Birds are nesting. I have to breathe through my mouth. We have had colds for months now. In the mornings, the last two mornings, a low mood has had to be turned over on waking. Just tiredness accreting into. Bad mood I suppose. We need to go away for a few days. I'd better write to Francis once more. And, and. My inhalations are raising and dropping the pressure in my ears. I might never see Fritz again. Or I might see him often. A branch is hanging by a fold of bark, broken off by the storm, but not completely.

It is hard to say how this is attached to productivity, more a rendering of now. A rendering of daily changes. Hardly offering anything at all. Feelings pass, affections pass. Or not pass, let's say, and stay in motion. There is movement to be felt, to be noticed. There is also need which has no inner form. Giulia sleeps in a bed built with her own hands.

It is 4.56 a.m. Vivian is good at going in and staying in the guitar. I always keep one foot out, always watching, as if something may happen when I am in there, in this place of my own making after all, keep an eye out in case some management needs to be done. It's an illusion, right? I am in there, immersed, and I can get out anytime I like. But something, paranoid litter, stops me. So I keep looking in two directions, in the guitar but always outside as well. Not a balance, a divide. I am not sure I like immersion, I prefer to look around myself, herself, looking around at what? At *now!* Maybe this is the thing about noise. The present is unstructuring, is a noise, and so nothing is built, well, except practice, getting better at the here and now.

Let's begin. Guitar! means, Hello! This is how you learn to speak.

When something is flat and round, not spherical,
not collapsible or collapsed, on only one plane, not
a solid, a shape, not patterned, not decorated, not a
disc, what is it?

A hole?

Can Ba touch Guitar?

Here a balloon touches a sound hole!
Here a round belly touches a bud!
Here an egg touches a mouth!
Here a lantern touches an iris!
Here a bubble touches a wheel!
Here a sphere touches a circle!

It is 5.41 a.m. I have been wondering if, with the right listener, you could live with just two words.

It is 12.55 p.m. Blossom is opening on the pum-tree.
The buds only appeared a week ago, now they open.
Yesterday was warmer, enough to leave my coat
behind. If I could stay here forever I would. Henry
is coming to talk to me about work. My eyes are
loose in their sockets, they twist and ache. Sinusitis.
I am so happy. This is a lot but it is true. Waking up I
am full, before sleep I am empty. Then I stop. Where
is Isobel? Where is her long hair and supreme smile?
I am going to lie down now on the floor. Vivian is
sleeping onwards. I always know where he is. Where
is Luca, or Louis, or

It is 11.53 a.m. The clouds are moving fast overhead. Noona is often in the guitar. In the guitar, she is hard to get to. My fingers are barely long enough to tweeze her out through the strings. This is, I believe, what untunes the guitar each day, Noona's potholing. I know the sounds now. I can hear her plummet from the other end of the house. She makes a clatter as her plastic body drops onto the wood, echoing as she rolls to a standstill. Then a pause. Then Vivian's pronounced, Uh-oh!

Noona came to the park with us today. A tractor was moving vast bags of woody material into the back of a truck. When the gardeners went for tea break Noona was placed face down on the hub of a big wheel, Uh-oh! Then retrieved and cuddled. Phenomenal Noona, she looked so very small and powerful lying there.

It is 8.24 p.m. I just filed Vivian's nails into a safe, blunt curve. He is so deeply asleep he can do nothing to protest. Lin suggested I do this, I was sure he would wake. The guitar is on the living room carpet where it should not be. Overnight it must go in the cupboard where its power can be contained. Much like the booth, I suspect the guitar is a space of amplification, but also of containment, containment of surplus disturbance.

I noticed that everything new which enters this house must be challenged by the guitar, must be worked a little on the threshold, must be introduced to the rigour of the guitar before it can settle and find a place in Vivian's world. This morning, we are leaving for a few days. Away on the train, away together, horse, truck, Noona, Inez and Tiberon and, I have not thought of everything or everyone. It is light in the mornings now, which is good for me. Although I moved onto my desk, and now the large computer obscures the tree and the pum-blossom.

No need to read on unless you miss my voice and want to listen to me for a while longer.

It is 12.28 p.m. We are not yet finished being exhausted since we arrived back.

It is 5.50 a.m. Vivian is sleeping. I am chewing
some bread. I don't want to talk to anyone. I don't
even want to talk to you. I thought that perhaps
this conversation, this practice, might be useful to
write down, to pass on. But, just sitting here, maybe
passing nothing on is better. My ears are full. Is there
a way for writing to make silence? Not the silence
of reading but silence inside, to silence thinking, not
a silent thought, which would be no thought at all.
Huh. Silence in the wake of a thought. A thought
that sponsors a silence. Pictures do that. Karen will
be sleeping right now, giving her thoughts back to
herself. I just keep looking and looking and my eyes
keep seeing, seeing, seeing. I have moved my desk
into the cupboard. There is a rainbow on the side
of the train tunnel with a rabbit sitting on top. A
mouse sits on the grassy verge. London is paused.
A bus and a black cab are circling. Play sand is stuck
to the soles of our feet and I am wondering – if the
birds stopped where would my thoughts go. Peta is
asleep, her hair smells of sea. Chloe has arrived, she
is wondering if she should come back here to live.
James and Kath are in Barry Island. Gail is sleeping
soundly against Bernd. Sleeping, sleeping. No-no is
as inscrutable as ever. Dear No-no, I think I am on
the other side of something. How do I know-know?
Because I can hold this thought, and I can think the
thought of looking backwards without falling asleep.

I have nothing to say except, *this* happened.

It is 6.40 a.m. All I can hear is rain and

How many times did I drink from a glass before I
learnt how to tighten my bottom lip just enough.

It is 11.26 a.m. The conversation I am having with this guitar is in my imagination. This guitar is absolutely not a guitar and absolutely real. Out from the empty space inside this guitar comes the noise I make, I made, just a second ago. I put the noise in there, away beyond my touch, I touched this guitar, its strings or its wooden box, and it sends noise from its inside back out to me, quick, quick! I do not speak a second language either.

It is 11.01 a.m. I got talking to another mother at the swings. She asked what I had on the following week and I said, Nothing. Then I said, I'm going to go and make some noise. I emphasised 'noise', that's when she lit up. I could see her excitement but not feel it. Like, Oh, look at me, I'm the person who is doing this exciting thing. Then she wanted to know where I was going to make this noise because you can't just make noise anywhere you like, can you?

Did I mention my glue ear?

It is 3.15 a.m. I can't sleep. The wind is getting up outside. God, I'm awake. Where did the booth come from? How did it get in there? Who made it? Does Isobel know? These thoughts have been built around the booth, it's like a diving bell. I was deaf, partially so, as a child. Is a child deaf? As a child, like them, was a me who dressed as a child. Is a child partially so? What is a child? I was deaf is a child? When I was a child I was deaf. I was deaf. Nite.

It is 12:03 p.m. I've been earning a living from transcription for years. It's a strange education in listening because what you hear nobody else hears and was never meant to be heard either.

For a long time my ears were nobody's concern. But when my hearing was corrected, at the age of seven, in flooded a surplus of clarity. This is how I discovered there is more. And this more is something I notice when transcribing, because transcription is a revealing of *more*. That which is not taken up by the speaker or the listener, the debris of conversation, is suddenly met.

So transcription is a form of listening, to what? At first to nothing. Nothing more than what is said. So there is not much to it, just follow the words, listen for the next word, and transcribe it onto a page. And what if a word does not come? Wait. Just like the speaker waits for a word to enter their thoughts, I wait for their word to enter my ears. A hesitation becomes hesitates. A sigh becomes sighs. Everything goes down to my fingers because I touch type when I transcribe from a recording. I touch the type and the word goes down. It touches down. No sooner has one word landed than the next is on its way. If the voice is fast, I race until I am outrun and then press pause. I listen again because one of two things has happened. I was either left behind, the sentence speeding on ahead, the transcriber out of puff, or I sense something is wrong. Something put down badly. So I need to go back and listen again. Some phrase more mine than theirs. Some confidence of mine not theirs. A struggle commences. For comprehension? Theirs and mine. D'you know what I mean?

I go back and listen again. Their words fall out of predictable rhythms, settling at angles with my expectations, bits clatter. And when the voice I am transcribing falters in this way, excited by unruly forces, the utterance will not wait in an orderly manner in my memory for the moment it takes to put it down. Because the unruly utterance is hard to hear. I am so trained by being human to hear sense, that transcribing non-sense, or the sense which is imminent, takes – I listen again.

And here is something, in the interests of getting it right, capturing the words accurately, I have unlearned listening. Learned to hear the outpouring that only means, I am here! To listen more intently when words fail and flare. Nagen-nagen. When a repetition urges forward some distant concern. Is this making any sense?

Transcription depends on what you are listening for, and what you are listening for changes as you do more listening. The listening is threefold: listening for my own impatience with the detail, listening for errors and listening for fallen words. If I type at the

same speed most people speak, it's the listening that
takes time. This unearthly listening, all by yourself,
is perhaps like reading people or brings me closer
to the thoughtfulness of a narrator.

It is 2.49 p.m. I mean, so much happens without speech, this is one reason why it can be a bit like the outside of a problem, the wreck rather than the collision. This is one reason why speech can be so true when it is at odds with events. Might the transcriber be able to listen out for the collisions between people, between a person and the world, or between a person and their own vocalising.

He has no word for other children.

It is 1.45 a.m. Vivian has kicked me out of bed again. He starts to turn clockwise around the axis of his belly until his feet reach my ribs, then he gently, gently stretches, finding deep in the cave of his sleep something at his toes, he kicks to push it away. And I am slowly displaced onto my desk. Hello!

It is 11.33 a.m. and it was so cold outside this morning I did not want to stop moving. Just sitting, stretching out my muscles now feels

It is 2.23 a.m. Alice, I am trying to remember if we hugged before we parted. We must have done. Maybe not though, you looked so smart.

Dear Alice,

This address, this en-dear-ing of you by me, is a soft
command to think of you as I sit down to write.
A little like good posture. You are digging in your
garden and I sit down to watch. Hear you, because
it is the fine and heavy falling of particles and clods
I am listening to. You don't need to listen, you just
do it, but this heave and turn is a new vocabulary
I want to join in with.

It's early!

Because I do not play the guitar, nor do I want to,
I have this with. I do not play the guitar, I play *with*
the guitar. What is this with? What's with the *with*?
If I learn how to play where does with go? Does
with disappear, like a noise out of a sentence, and
what was with doing? I don't play a person or a
wooden bee. Once someone can make music on the
guitar, is with forgotten? Is noise the sound of with?
What is the work of with? Does music just conceal
the with-ness of *doing* the guitar, or is it that once
playing the guitar is underway, and music making
becomes effortless, the guitar and you merge and
the doing, the playing, is no longer *with* anything,
no friction, the guitar has vanished and you are
alone without with.

It is 4.30 a.m. I haven't been awake to write for a couple of months at least. The clouds are overstated, dazzling. Birds on the roofs opposite gather food and bearings for the morning ahead. It is mid-summer now and feels like another hot humid day beginning. Vivian has been up for two hours chanting, playing, wrestling me in bed, now he sleeps. Five minutes have passed and the pink sky has already vanished into clear blue. We will all leave the house soon and go away together. This will be the first time the house will be left totally alone since he was born. Bye-bye! Hey ho! In the sand is Daddy-doll, he is giving me the thumbs up. I think we all love each other for now. I'm going back to bed. Just the birds, no cars, no people. Maybe this is the last time this will happen.

It is 5.32 a.m. I have worked quite hard at keeping all kinds of noise at bay, at loving silence. But the Guitar! I have here and now, took shape in noise, took its form from noise, is made with noise.

It is 5.24 a.m. Write soon Chloe. Write soon Aman. Am I done?

Cause I've thought about it more since. Cause I just think it's a pretty exciting thing to do. I've thought about what I'd do. I think I've thought about it cause I wondered what I'd do if I had the chance. Trying to imagine how it'd feel. Cause I kinda went between thinking it could be really exciting or it could be, arghhhh, intimidating and full of fear. Waiting for me to step in. Settles. So, I thought it was an interesting, erm, proposal. I was just imagining myself in the situation, how I would be. You see, I flip between one and the other. I thought about what I'd do if I was the person speaking, and I've thought about what I'd do if I was the person listening, and trying to imagine how it'd feel. Hesitates. You'd have to be the person going first cause you're the one in control, and you know what it is you're there for, there's a purpose and a reason. To then thinking, what if there're big gaps. Waiting for me to speak. Settles. So what if you can't respond. How would you feel, how would you take it forward. Maybe I'd rather be the person who's not in control. Although there are so many decisions to be made together, before you meet. I must have been frowning as I tried to imagine what the preparations for a noise might be. You could just arrive somewhere and… Probably a room somewhere, which is… Not… It's just… It doesn't have to be anything special, other than just a room that isn't anybody's, it isn't yours or theirs, it's just kind of quite blank and… With not a lot in it, maybe soundproofed but maybe not. It isn't domestic, it isn't work related, it's somehow somewhere in between. But not social, I didn't imagine it being somewhere like out in the pub or a restaurant, somewhere much quieter. It has to be just the two of you, meeting, at an agreed time. And I guess you don't have the tools or the things you'd have around you if you were just having a normal conversation, like a packet of biscuits and a cup of tea. Erm, so it's all just paired back to just, just two people and their sounds, the sound of… This noise they're gonna make. Hesitates. And the very initial moments, walking into the space, the simple things like where d'you sit with the person, how d'you introduce yourselves, become significant. If there's no tools how the room itself becomes a tool. If there's no structure, how the time itself forms its own structure. And just what d'you end up doing? So, yeh, I probably imagined it more with a person you didn't really know so well. You'd start with small chat and then see where the small talk went. And I also thought about you in it, cause I don't know you very well, but I've never thought of you as someone who does small talk, but maybe that's cause we're always shouting at each other across the park. So, I was thinking, what if there's no small talk how d'you begin cause I think I'd probably

start with, How are you? How's your day been?
And, Isn't it shit that it's rained so much this last…
And then fall into, you know, and so, if there's no
small chat, how d'you ever get to anything more…
Meaningful? Laughs. Then I laugh. I hadn't thought
of noise as deep, but when she says this I can begin
to imagine this noise, the noise she's going to make,
and how she's going to get to make it. My default
setting is to ask questions, so. So, I know that's a
tactic. I don't even think about it now, it's just what
I do. This is how we talk, her questions, my fatigue,
no small talk, sprint to the swings, back to the slide.
But, also cause, I'm interested in people, and what
you do and how you think. I'm one of five sisters,
in fact I've got four sisters, five girls altogether. And
we all do it. Some of us to greater extents. But I've
got two sisters who are just, unbelievable at asking
direct questions. And, and, it being fine. It being.
They never disarm people, or make them feel
uncomfortable. They're really good at having
conversations. But being very direct and getting…
And getting to find out. Or, have conversations
about things. You'd be like, How did you do that?
Pauses, perhaps to think of her sisters. I think it's a
lovely thing. I think it's a very nice thing. To be able
to… To not intrude, you're not trespassing. You're
not being nosy. They're actually just really being
empathetic to what they hear. Maybe she's missing

them a bit. I guess, it's funny too. I'm just thinking about a couple of people. If I sat down with them they'd talk for a whole hour. You'd just have to sit them down and say, How you doing? and your whole afternoon would be filled. I quite like having conversations with those people. It kinda takes the pressure off you – off of me. It doesn't always happen, I mean, I think, I like. If I think about the people I'm closest to in my life, they're people who enjoy talking and they're people you don't have to try very hard with. But maybe, that just happens because they become friends over time. Uncertain pause, as if lost. But no, I think my best friends, and the people I love most, are people who enjoy talking, cause there's always something going on in the background, or the foreground, if you're paying attention. And not so much silence, cause silence is, you've got to work hard. To fill it. Sometimes you don't have the reserves to fill it. If they're the quiet type, imagine sitting with someone for hours. That'd be really difficult. But, yeh, I did, I went over it quite a bit in my head, thinking. I thought it was brave, I think it's brave! That's probably what I thought. And I thought it was brave because I probably couldn't imagine myself being somebody who could do it. To just have that time. I think it's exciting. I think the excitement is in just… erm… going off on kind of a short journey, you don't

know where you're gonna go, you don't know
whether you are leading or whether you're being
led. And uncertainty about where it leads to and
what the point of it is. Cause why do you have a
conversation? I guess different people have different
conversations for different reasons don't they. Just for
company, to learn something, to share something.
To preach. I'm trying to think about when I have
a good conversation, what is it? A good sense of
humour probably, to laugh, to feel something. I'm
thinking of the people I know well and really like
having conversations with, and then, then it would
just defeat the purpose to have them, to have this
with them would just be too out of the ordinary.
With this, I dunno, the uncertainty is in not
knowing if there will be words. So then it would
have to be somebody that I didn't know. And then
I'd have to think about why them in particular. And
then, if I was thinking about somebody in particular,
I'd have an agenda or a reason to talk to them but
there is no agenda or reason so I dunno. Maybe they
have time on their hands. But what if somebody else
unexpectedly volunteers themself. I really don't
know. I actually think it's quite hard thinking of
who it'll be. I'd have to think quite hard. And I
don't know what it is I would be really thinking
about. Maybe, well. Hesitates. Is this a cop-out to say
it'd be my husband? Erm. I have no idea where we

could meet. Maybe here. Not at home. Erm. But, no, that might be just too weird. I was just thinking… I was thinking about him because… I can't remember the last time we sat down and had a proper conversation. So, actually, there's something quite nice in thinking about having time to sit down and have a conversation about nothing, about everything, anything, to have silence too. It sounds like a thing we should probably do a hell of a lot more of. No, but I mean. It's almost. It's kind of. Not in a dutiful way. She is waiting for me to step in but I don't. When I say silence, I don't mean no sound, I mean a strange flattening of attention or something. You pay attention in a different way. Not thought. More waiting for the next thought to come along. A slowing down… A slightly… A different. Speed. If you've got hectic lives. Yeh. It could be exciting to. Almost a stop. You actually give each other time to be… silent. To make as much, or as little noise as you want. Or to work things out. Or to just have that moment to think. Hesitates. Because you are so used to having to respond immediately. To what it is that's going on. I think, err… Yeh. Fear. Excitement. Wonderment. Just. Trying to imagine how you'd be yourself in that situation. But also not having any rules. I guess, part of the excitement of thinking about it was just… Imagining not having any rules, that's how

I imagined it when you talked about it and, and…
Wondering what, where you end up at the end.

It is 4.15 p.m. I am navigating storms which would be better stormed.

You speak. Whispered. How do you do? Mellow
with a hushed formality. I think it's picking you
up. So, I would like to make some noise. Ticking.
Right now? Hesitates. Sometime? Soon? Settles.
Okay sounds good, what kinda noise would it be?
Ticking. Is it a musical noise or a percussive noise?
Maybe percussion and singing, maybe you start a
song and then I join in, what do you think? Ticking.
Maybe we can have harmonies in it, harmonies are
quite good, cause we've done that before with songs,
so maybe that's how we'd start and there might be
some percussion as well. Static. But, maybe it's best
not to plan it too much, we just improvise it. Plastic
clatter. When will we make this noise? Not tonight?
Maybe tomorrow? Is it going to be, hesitates, gentle
singing? Gentle noise? I keep wondering about
this no noise noise, does gentle noise go with no
consequence, is consequence getting to the nub
of noise, what has he done to my noise with his
'gentle', much more than just adding say 'quiet' or
'distant'. Sudden clatter, loud, nothing said. It might
have your singing which is quite gentle, I dunno
it might be meditative with a bit of rhythm to it,
he is changing direction, I heard that song on the
radio yesterday you used to sing to Vivian you used
to sing that really well so maybe you can start you
could do that. I do not remember singing really
well. Maybe it sounds like the song you used to sing

about the storm coming over the horizon, gentle clicking starts, I quite like the harmonies I did with that one. No harmonies, no thank you, low hissing climbs, drops, settles. Ticking. Are you still recording me? Whispered, gently curious. Oh. Settles. Well that's what I'd do, I think some harmonies are quite good, inhales. Hummm-hum-hum-hum-hummm ascending. Hummm-hum-hum-hum-hummm descending, something like that, yeh. Ticking. Well it depends if you want Vivian to join in or not cause he'd probably join in if there's something going on that's interesting or we'd have to do it quietly, we can do quiet singing, hissing, very quiet, I suppose. That's the other option. Static. Yeh, quiet noise so not loud noise, ticking, so noise doesn't have to be loud so it could be gentle noise like, ticking, maybe that's a good idea, noise of the night, kinda noise that hopefully doesn't wake anybody up, very faint clicking or knocking which I can't identify, something is resting upon something else lifting with the rhythm of his breathing. Hissing and ticking lost under a whoosh, a car coming over the hill. Yeh, maybe the way to go, ting! You could even use the water bottle, ting! Percussion, yeh? Could be quite good, knocking settles. I dunno, whatever we've got nearby, hesitates, dry scraping, maybe that, maybe this, heavy, papery bangs, scratchy dragging, like chalk on a board, ticking. Yeh, those're my ideas.

Ticking. Tup-tup-tup, tup-tup-tup, his finger tups
out a steady rhythm with a skip now and again,
continues with the ticking of his wristwatch, like
that, those kinda noises. Hum. Lots of options.
Tap-tap-tap, tap-tap-tap, his finger finds another
surface, could be quite quiet, still interesting! We'd
have to deal with the consequences of a big noise.
Laughing. Wake the neighbours! whispered. That's
what one of the consequences would be wouldn't
it. Ticking. Mmm, ting! I like the sound of bottles
and metal objects like bells and things that've got
some liquid in them, hesitates, glasses and things, car
whooshing over the hill, ticking, think I'm getting a
numb leg, clattering, numb calf, you alright, numb
knee, uhuh, clunking, banging, shifting weight,
settles. Even the lap, the tummy's quite good
sometimes, tap-tap-tap, tap-tap-tap, yeh it's like a
drum, could work? A long pause here, he is finding
some new direction. Just some thoughts, to add to
the, cauldron. Laughs. Concoction! More ticking,
he's still searching. Even scratching the beard, bristly
rubbing, it's a very quiet noise, bristly rubbing, see
how quiet a noise you could make, sticky mouth,
that still gets picked up, could be interesting, see
how quiet we could sing, as well, ticking. D'you
want to make loud noise? What did you imagine?
I dunno, when you said lots of noise I thought
at first that might be loud noise but that doesn't

necessarily mean it has to be loud noise, car on the hill. It could be any kinda noise lots of quiet noise or subtle noise, slowing down. So could be any kinda noise couldn't it? What d'you think? That's what I thought maybe quiet noise for practical reasons, ticking, cause of Vivian, well it might be different if we were out, it depends where we were, Vivian would come with us wouldn't he so we'd have to go to the park, play the drums, there're some musical things there or we'd have to improvise when we went out. Sticks. Railings. So could be a louder noise, unfortunately it's the wrong season for leaf stomping but all the leaves have been soaked turned to mulch, suppose you could do puddles, so there're plenty of outdoor noises we could make, we could go in the tunnel and make some omus, omus, omus. Ticking. All kinds. He's waiting for me to step in here. What'd you think? He wants me to step in, to step into this tunnel walk and shout loud so an echo travels up and around and through and out the other side to meet him. We could go by ourselves I say. Where would Vivian be? What if he was playing with Karen. Alright, well then we could do anything we wanted couldn't we, go to the studio, could play loud music, use instruments, record it. Guitars. We could try anything, even drums, suppose we could do different things couldn't we. He is about to change direction. Be more experimental. He is changing direction, ticking. Is it a project?

It is 2.11 p.m. I am struck by soft squeaks of polystyrene. I feel met!

Guitar! she says, when she could have said, Hello!
The Technician, replies, Guitar!

Technically speaking, he is not The Technician
at this moment, this being the end of the day, he
is just someone who likes noise. And she is not
The Musician either, she is just someone who wants
to make some noise. He pulls himself out from under
his desk and goes to greet her.

She smiles a sure and wide smile from where she
is. This scatters his momentum, pausing him, while
she takes in the recording studio from the open door.

The Technician sort of hangs there, on hold,
watching her look, look, look, his arms neither loose
nor tense, just unemployed at his sides.

She is looking beyond him, bright and nosy and
ready to leave if she so feels. She sees all the cables

and stuff, his stuff still switched on, on, on – oh – sound is still flickering inside the mixing desk, the lamp is still pouring over his notes, noise is spilling out of his headphones and onto the desk, sometimes he loses track of time.

Guitar, guitar, she says, and takes a step towards him.

Guitar, guitar, he replies, stepping to meet her.

It is symmetrical, swift and strong, they hug, they let go. He finds his pockets. She balances, one leg twisted around the other, it is not as uncomfortable as it looks.

The Technician peers around her with mock curiosity, searching for something, Guitar? he asks.

She stretches out her arms as wide as they will go and her fingers reach out even further to grapple comically with the enormous, empty space she is suddenly holding, Guitar!!! she replies.

The Technician laughs at the scale of her invisible guitar.

She doubles his laughter with her own. She is laughing because she is surprised he is laughing. He had forgotten she was coming. She sighs over the top of his laughter, lowering their volume to a soft, soft whisper, Guitar, guitar, guitar…

Here they were, at five-to-two, standing on and off and between scattered rugs, insulated behind foam-packed walls, without windows, unimpressed by each other, laughing quite loudly, then observing the inverse of their laughter with no plan or chasm to cross.

She had said, at first to herself, I want to make some noise. I want to surprise myself with the noise I can make. And, at first, she couldn't think of anyone who would not be frightened by what she meant. This was not about letting anything out. More like putting something out. She didn't know how she was going to do this. She is not musical. This is the confusing part. To get help she would need to talk different. She doesn't know the words to ask for what she wants. Who might be able to second-guess? Who might listen? Someone she does not have to bother too much about. She does not want to bother too much about herself either for that matter. And noise is, she realises, a sound that makes no sense, yet. Hard to coax. Hard to say where it might appear. What is different about her noise is how big it will be. What is big? Well, bigger than her. Beyond her past, towards her future. Although, being noisy is easy and silence requires some practice. She has been practising for a while now, bringing a noise into being may be a bit of a wish in a well. She does not know how to do this with him, or anybody else for that matter. Noise would be an honest way of behaving right now. Now, something seems to be happening. The lack of any plan is exciting, although a plan is forming because of this one word they have in common.

To The Technician, she said, Let's meet at your studio and make noise. He agreed, although he found this puzzling because that is what he liked to do, and she did something else, walking or yoga, or there was her love of dance. The Technician is in love most of the time, with noises which refuse to reveal their means, with his guitars, with the latest known feelings of his son Vivian and with the unearthly silence deep inside the recording studio's belly – his son, Vivian! He loves Vivian!

Right now Vivian is playing with his guitar, dropping a painted wooden bee onto its strings to hear the jumble of bounces it makes as it finds a path between the strings and down through the sound hole, rattling to a standstill somewhere behind the shadows inside. Then he points to Auntie Karen. She tilts the guitar until the bee rolls back into view, scissoring her fingers she grasps the felt wings and guides the bee slowly up through the strings and back into Vivian's hand. Again! His mother is picking up his father from work, they are talking in a strange way.

The Technician was worried they would find nothing to do together. The Musician was worried they would have nothing to say. She says nothing. She shouts, Guitar! Guitar! Guitar! the word sounds great in there.

The Technician could not smile any more if he tried. He hangs his head, he is actually too shy to show her his happiness. The word is just so funny now, and immense, and cute. He tries to capture all of this, he shouts back, Guitar! Guitar! Guitar! Oh – it's a bit disappointing, to both of them. He is trying but, obviously stymied by embarrassment. He is so very awkward and shy, shy, shy.

She has another go, Guitar! Guitar! Guitar! This time she sounds more passionate, less desperate.

He tries harder too, Guitar! Guitar! Guitar! It is a little better, closer to singing, but still hollow.

She takes a deep breath, Guitar! Guitar!! Guitar!!! Oh – she already peaked. Her last attempt was her best and now she has nowhere left to go, and this directionless arrow lands at a silly angle. Silly and maybe angry.

Suddenly he looks all serious or blank or thoughtful. He hears something she does not hear and has stopped. What is it? He isn't sure, like her voice went a bit mad and interesting. His own selfish attraction takes over. He wants to listen again. Beckoning her, he says, Guitar!

Her mouth is dry, she needs a glass of water. She squeaks an uncomfortable, Guitar!!! Nope. No arrow this time.

He tries something else entirely, Guitar! Guitar! Guitar! Guitar! making a rhythm.

Guitar! Guitar! Guitar! Guitar! she joins in.

Together their metronome sinks into the foam, the room watches them slow.

She exhales, Guitar!

Guitar! is boring.

Guitar! is beautiful.

Guitar! doesn't mean anything.

Anyone can play guitar.

The meaning is dying.

He tries a sliding, Gui-tarrrr.

She blasts, Guitar!!! Guitar!!! Guitar!!!

He shrieks, Guitar! Guitar! Guitar! He has no ideas left.

She couldn't care less.

He sounds upset about something.

They stop.

Her eyes travel slowly over his face. Her mouth makes a silent, You okay?

The Technician, who can tolerate much disturbance, does not feel at ease with this shouting, especially from her. He makes a small, unhappy mouth, then makes a small, happy one, all from under a worried brow. Although the shouting is empty, it is still shouting. He slowly raises his right hand up in front of his face and gently touches the tip of his nose with his index finger, he mimes a faux sneeze and says, Gui-tar! rather than Ait-choo!

She laughs.

He walks over to her, and with a poker face, places the same finger on the tip of her nose, she sneezes a melodic, Gui-tarrr!

She can sing!

She has sung every day since Vivian was born. Singing to her son surprised her. She could not sing at school therefore she could not sing. She imagined he would flinch. As it turns out she has a lovely voice. The Technician often agrees, You know Vivian, your Mum has a lovely singing voice. And her speaking voice is more pliant too. She finds she can modulate its softness and build a melody out of talk, gently shifting in and out of song, in a very, very small opera.

Now her nose really does tickle. She has to wait for the itch to subside.

He thinks she is thinking.

She is thinking about the itch, and how if she sneezes now, she will be flattening his sneezing joke, undoing his spontaneity. Or maybe just making it last longer.

She does not play the guitar. Nor does she want to. But now she has found this Guitar, spat it out, and he has passed it back, back and forth several times, it is quite unrecognisable. Quite different now, for her at least.

Guitar, guitar, guitar, guitar, guitar, guitar, she asks, squinting at the acoustic guitars propped against their shadows around the room. She doesn't want to play them but there they are, ready in the darkness.

The Technician rides his swivel chair across the floor towards her. He gets up and switches on the lights, it sounds like a hundred tiny glass brains waking up, staggering to attention, colliding in the brightness.

Guitar! Guitar! Guitar! she says riding a wave of enthusiasm for this beautiful, unwitting noise.

He switches the lights off.

Then on again.

The noise is chaotic. They, the brains, are still drunk. She watches them flicker into consciousness. She points her eyes back at the switch.

He flicks it off.

Then on once more.

This is Guitar! They found this Guitar! It's a great noise. They are doing this together. This Guitar! is nothing like anything they have done before. If they were to go back, try to remember when they had last found a noise together, maybe when they first met, they would not find another even nearly as good as this one. This occasion is a first. Once more then no more. They look up, the glass tubes are clinking without breaking, inside the fluorescence is happening, figuring out if it wants to be or not.

The Technician is underprepared. But for what? For feeling lost. This isn't a date. He stops himself.

He was going to say something funny. He sits back down. There is a long, long silence. It is very quiet, like someone's been told off. He is building a wall to stop himself wondering what might – or might not – happen. It is painful, this hesitation. Impossible to stop trying to be normal. What's niggling him is the idea of a destination. Here is this new abyss called Guitar! But there is the old idea of a destination, which he never reaches anyway. Where is this Guitar! going? What does she want? The idea of competition keeps coming into his mind. If he can just get to the end of the conversation without saying anything else then he has sort of made it. He wonders, if he can do this well can they in some way win? Now there is the possibility of winning, he wants to keep going.

She is watching him. He is making a face. Could be something, could be nothing, an expression of determination, a twinge, a pivot, as if he misses a step in a dream and wakes from falling, returning with a start.

Guitar? she asks.

He does not reply.

She gently dips and cranes forwards. She keeps going until he cannot not look back at her. He does not look at her. Is he okay? This is her caring face. She is slightly annoyed. She realises she was really enjoying the conversation now it has halted.

She got talking to another mother at the swings. The other mother asked what she had on the following week and she said, Nothing. Then she said, I'm going to go and make some noise. She emphasised 'noise', that's when the other mother lit up. She could see the other mother's excitement but not feel it. Like, Oh, look at me, I'm the person who is doing this exciting thing. She *is* doing this exciting thing.

Is it unpleasant for him sitting here? Maybe they should have met out somewhere. Not here, not home, somewhere else. He is doing something strange and subtle, swaying gently without looking up. The room is cold. One or two brains cough, the last ones to wake, this is the end of their 'on' point.

The walls listen for more noise. The walls can presumably sing. Having absorbed so many voices, they can join in with this guitar chorus. He is doing something. He is tapping his heel, rhythmically. Is he singing Guitar! Guitar! Guitar! to himself?

When she walked in the room, she saw a sheet of paper over there above his desk with what looked like a list, and she wondered if they were a thing he had to remember To Do. She looks again. It is a fire drill.

He stops singing to himself. He swivels around to see what she was looking at behind him. Guitar? he says. He reaches over for the sheet of paper and gathers a stray pencil. He flips the paper over to find the blank side then hunches over the desk, working away for a while, shielding his drawing with a crooked arm.

She has been not thinking about this all week. She hasn't mentioned it once, to him. And it is possible he has also made this into a secret. As it turns out, this is as good as a secret can get. A secret neither noticed. What would that be? An ignorance. She has been mixing words, trying to grasp the correct one. So 'got' needs to be 'have'. Sometimes she does this smoothly, while talking, self-correcting while she is mid flow. But often she has to shape the right one while abandoning the wrong one, creating a strange bungee between the beginning of one word and the end of another. A surprise. What is he drawing? She is going to ask him. Now they have found this guitar to play with, which is way better than anything she could have come up with by herself, she is reconsidering his properties. The Guitar! was her idea. Or she just said it first. She imagines how to say, Guitar? if her question is going to carry. What is he doing? Drawing? She could have not turned up. Perhaps then he would have remembered. He is the colour of lint. His hair is no colour at all! Grey sweatshirt, nothing on it to read. His jeans and trainers are covered in pale, dry powder. Cement? She is about to ask.

He looks back up to say something. Oh! she is going to say something. He waits. She is about to speak. Or is she? How will she say Guitar!

She asks, Guitar?

He flashes his drawing at her. It is a violin. He reconsiders. He adds a bit more. Then raises the picture to show properly. A bubble! The violin has a thought inside a bubble. Where the thought ought to be is a tiny drawing of a guitar. That is not all. He hunts around again. Through the centre of the drawing he pokes the point of a blade and starts to work a pair of scissors round and round until a spiral of paper springs out and falls to the floor. He is finished! Now the violin has the round soundhole of a guitar.

He can draw. You can really believe this violin. You could take it for a walk. Guitar! Guitar! Guitar! she says as he looks at her over the drawing. She is not so sure though. The cutting has done something disagreeable to the life of the drawing. Made it too much part of their world. Maybe that's what he wanted. The violin is not what it was. And she can't help but wonder about the part of the drawing which is missing, the little spiral of soundhole he just swept up and dropped into the empty bin, Ting!

She walks over and stares into the bin. Alone, at the bottom, is the crooked spiral. She doesn't like things in empty bins. She knows the bin's been placed there for this very occasion but the spiral makes her skin prickle. She is being odd. She knows he knows what she is doing. Only if they're empty. Mainly if they're cylindrical. The volume of the bin sort of pushes back. The spiral drop has interrupted the bin. The bin was intensely concentrating on being empty and now the moment is ruined. She knows the work of the bin is to hold rubbish. But an empty bin's work is different. Its labour is more spiritual. When empty, a bin is not holding nothing, it's holding onto itself. The crooked spiral is not rubbish either. It is a fragment of the violin, it is what was stopping the violin being a guitar and now it is the violin's corporeal injury. Capacity! The spiral is interrupting the bin's capacity to hold emptiness. And the bin is withholding the spiral from its capacity to be more than the mere obstacle that keeps the violin dreaming of being a guitar. The spiral drop ting was amplified by the bin, as if it, the crooked spiral, had discovered the sound of itself, its own voice, despite being at the moment just dead wood cast off by another form's reinvention.

She reaches down, collects the crooked spiral and drops it into the bin again. Ting! Guitar! she says. She looks back to The Technician. He is loosening, then tightening, the neck of a mic stand, tilting the microphone downwards. He picks it up and brings it over.

Guitar! he says, then hangs the head of the microphone deep inside the bin.

He gets lost in switches and plugs. She stares at the probe stationed inside the bin. He taps on a keyboard and gives her a nod. This time, when the spiral hits the bin the ting explodes.

He looks through her, some part of him, the professional annex, is busy calculating what was produced with the position of the microphone as it is. He adjusts the stand, Guitar! he says. She drops the spiral once more. The room returns a metallic thunder. What is amplified is not what she heard. This is beyond anything her ears could glean from falling paper. A relationship between paper and aluminium, between spiral and cylinder, something she knew nothing of before the microphone intervened, is revealed. This noise is Guitar! The taste of coffee is Guitar! A ripe pear with cheese is Guitar!

He stoops down and brings the microphone up into alignment with her head. She looks at its shiny, foiled dome. The Technician twists it towards her chin. She keeps still. He attaches a pop screen and bends it into position between her and the mic.

He makes an instruction to himself, do not use another word until she does. His timing is different from hers. He is working mainly through memories of what she said to him late at night to make sense

of this. Good, the mic is in position. His sense of
humour is different. She knows a few jokes but he
doesn't find them funny, she says they are better
than his jokes but they are just things that happened
with no punchline. They do not even have the
features of a joke. Like the one that goes – he
cannot remember what they talked about last week.
He remembers her saying something about a fog,
being in love with fog and wanting to make a lot of
noise the size of fog. An alarm goes off. No. A siren.
And she wakes up. She can sing. Was it a dream to
do with the future or the past?

They have plateaued.

She doesn't want anything from him. She thinks
he is happy working in here. The position of the
mic is good. Thank you, she thinks, now I will
make some noise. He is stopping something from
happening by standing there. The thing won't
happen because he is standing in the way. So she
may not discover what the noise is until he lies
down.

Guitar! she says, and points to the floor.

He has an idea what she means. He wants to ask.
Maybe his questions don't matter.

Guitar! she says again, and points to a rug.

He reaches for the cushion on his chair, slings it
on the carpet, lies down on his back, tucks his hands
behind his head and closes his eyes.

The fire engine's wheels pinch the strings of the guitar together when Vivian slides them up and down the fretboard, this back and forth action actually makes a nee-naw.

She is thinking what to do now. She feels giddy. She leans into the microphone and says, Guitar means

Your
may cause
compliments
but who's
complaining
New Autumn
Wardrobe
DRESSIN
HE NATION
NCER.COM
CUBE

It is 10.08 p.m. Your hand is wet so you drop the guitar, sounds like justice falling on a bonnet. Good sounds made in error because you do not know much. Tolerate all this grim and flimsy wrongdoing. Then go back and wonder at what you can do without any skill, with the friction of a beginner.

It's quite a strange thing, I dunno, finding someone you don't know. And then, how do you get to know somebody you don't know? I dunno. Maybe you put some advert out in a newspaper, maybe that's a bit complicated, maybe it is just a friend of a friend. I guess when I said, I'd like to be that person, I thought it would be quite an odd but yet interesting thing to do, to arrange a time with someone you don't know, to walk into a room, decide this isn't normal from the get-go and you both agree to that. But then you find out about each other through this really contrived situation. Or maybe it's not about finding out about each other, maybe it's about some kind of reciprocal situation when you each get something from it. I don't know, yeh, but I like the idea of an 'on-point'. Like you come and you're definitely there for that period of time so you kinda got to make something happen. It's not unstructured like, an hour goes by at work and you do nothing, this is quite tightly structured with a wide open-ended realm of possibilities that could come out of it. It's nice to think about it being an activity you'd carry on forever, for the rest of your life. I quite like that. I imagine you wouldn't always meet as frequently, you wouldn't have to because you'd get better with practice. Force is not the right word but to have this relationship which is just this time you ask each other for and you don't speak of this at any other point, it's just, it seems really full of potential. Yeh. I'd kinda thought about doing something like that myself actually, a long time ago, to just see what would happen. Certainly not with people I didn't know, I didn't know how to get to that point, well I didn't even think about people who I could maybe make music with. It took a long time to convince someone, then arrange a time and for that to get delayed and then it just never sort of happened. With that, I think it was an uncertainty about what you'd do, an expectation. I think the person I was speaking to maybe liked the idea but the actual doing of it was less exciting. The not knowing what would happen was I think the thing that put them off. It's not easy to be in a situation that you – not many people try to put themselves in situations where they don't know what is going on, right? It's uncomfortable – or not, or really good. But it's rare I guess. But it's not on anyone's terms I guess, I mean one person has to approach the other about it but you don't really know what the terms are because it's this unstructured time. You don't know if the other person has real plans for it or ideas for it, yeh. But you've got motivations, right. You want something to come out of it. Or maybe you don't look at your motivations, I dunno. Or it might not go anywhere. It's so hard to grasp what we are actually talking about. It is hard to grasp what they are talking about but I think they are talking about hope. I guess the start is maybe not, I don't really have an idea for that but you would just want it to go somewhere. Maybe it doesn't matter so much about starts, there isn't a situation where you can just both decide at the same moment, you can never have the idea at exactly the same time but I don't think that's a problem at all. There's two of you, someone suggests something, and it just carries on and it's not, I can't imagine an ideal starting point, it would just have to be reasonably natural enough, although it is never going to be natural, it's quite an 'on-point' encounter. It probably goes quite quickly, I guess you have to have a starting point each time, how do you pick that up, is there a phrase or a sound, or motif you return to? Does it happen quite naturally or is there. Lots of silence. On the way in there's probably chat, but then there's that moment the door closes. Then somebody makes the first sound, and somebody makes another, and so on. Or not. But I think you're right, the start can fade really quickly into an afterthought, it doesn't have to be in the front of this other person's mind at all, and that's probably personality. You just go to someone with an idea, or a sort of framework and then you can both fill it, and you negotiate. You negotiate what you do, you decide if you want to make noise or if you want to do nothing of the sort.

Or sometimes you can both take photographs, or write things down or whatever. It's something you can alter but it's also something beyond your control because it is so outside your normal interactions and your routine. You could have conversations you wouldn't, you just really wouldn't otherwise. You decide to go into that space, kind of to be put on the spot by each other and it's quite, yeh, there's something about it being this reflective time, it's quite exciting. Because you'd not be having free-flowing conversations I don't imagine – you might, I dunno. There's something exciting about having this kinda friendship without being a friend. Without having any *ouft* stuff that comes along with being a friend. You know, LIFE, I dunno. You're not reliant on each other or something. You each give that time and that's – weirdly tidy. Erm. But it's like you can check in at a different pace to your normal routine, or your normal, the things that are going on. You can step outside, and the idea to be able to do that ongoing, ad infinitum, is like really appealing. Also, probably quite difficult as well, quite an endurance to that commitment. You'd need an 'out-point' in case it became some kind of slog. You know, if you both played together but you felt like your imagination was exhausted. But I guess you wouldn't put a limit on how long it's going to go on for, you wouldn't say we have to do this until the end of days. You know what I mean? You wouldn't set that out as a stipulation. Yeh, I don't foresee that many other problems. He is invited to do this thing without edges. It's funny, like I was saying, yeh it's funny that, hypothetically it sounds really good – but then in actuality – well, maybe the problem I see then is commitment. The ability to actually make that commitment. And the anxiety of thinking about who you would do it with, and, do you commit to that person even if it turns out there is zero, nothing in common, and nothing happens, maybe it just stops or finishes in those circumstances. I think I would probably like to be approached rather than approach someone, thinking about who is quite a big, yeh, task. Umm. Umm. I'd need to think about it. I wonder if it would be strange, even though we don't know each other that well, maybe us talking about this process changes it? Or makes it different. I'm not sure it would really. I think I would. I think I really would actually. I think I would probably need it to be erm, not super regular, but regular enough so that I wouldn't forget – not that I'm planning on forgetting but just so there's some kind of thing to keep it ticking. To do this with a few different people would be really fascinating. Maybe you want to do that? Why don't you do it? I guess I'm putting that on you. I guess I'm lazy actually. I'm hypothetically capable of doing lots of things but when it comes to it then, yeh. I've been really crap in the past with saying I can do loads of things and then not actually being able to do them when it came to it. Saying, yes, to too many things. So I am trying to not engage with as many things as I used to, to hopefully have a deeper engagement with what I am trying to engage with. And when? Maybe not a weekend. Maybe after work, before work, feels quite important to have a day at least to do nothing. There will be a certain kind of tension which is not relaxing. Do you agree? We can say what something's not. It's hard to be precise, to say what this is. It is nice to be asked to do this. Erm, I thought I would think about it but maybe it doesn't need thinking about.

It is 10.02 p.m. You do not have to build from the ground up, and you do not need any special tools either, guitars can be made from anything anywhere.

Poor talk sunk my ears. Sunk them deep in a cake.
Leave town! was one thought. Go now! another.
I was navigating storms which would have been
better stormed. I was not lazy, you were not inept,
although you had found uses for your awkwardness.
In the end, it was our bad rhythm that was hard
won. Being frighteningly awkward together, again
and again, we did this. And now? We live side by
side, we remain changed. The habit does not come
with a method of ending so we did not end – sad
isn't it, no end yet we lapsed, we drifted, which I
blame on fatigue. I am trying to work out if there
was anything unloving about what we did.

   Start with a natural equality. Find someone with
NO DOUBTS how equal they are to you. Keep an
eye out for resistance and opposition, they are bright

signs. How do you know? Once you meet, together you might forget the time. In social life, you might say something like, Stop doing that! and move away. STAY. Push each other until you feel your strength. I wanted just really just to stop reiterating myself. I wanted to do the only thing I am any good at, talking to strangers. Looking back, I wonder if you were a bit trapped in my idea. Do not consider your introduction too carefully. Speak! Change anything you like, go ahead, this is not a technique. Ask to meet. Give permission. Say, Yes, without asking why. This is not going to happen overnight. So the cart can start slow, clumsily, with no style. The start itself will feel wrong, as though you can do nothing well.

What did you expect? Seek no terms of agreement. Never be rude. Do not be unkind. You found the noise frustrating. You would have preferred me to be more intellectual or cleverer when I was just trying to find out if I could make you laugh. And, now I write this, I realise maybe that is why we told each other jokes. You bite your lip instead of laughing. Whereas my humour tends towards provocation. The wind getting up outside is Guitar! Maybe we only made each other nervous. Sometimes you were too much and that could be funny. More means, More!

Now I really value our conversation. Begin with an ask. For almost two years I spoke in a different way. My social skills were compact, I wanted to listen, I used two or three words, they were enough. I thought, if we can do this here, then surely we can do this in the rest of our lives. We tried. Our attempts failed. Not everyone can meet you. I am not saying we were unqiue, or this was specific to us, but I think we were odd in the same way, in some ways the noise was simply the sound of our desperation. Guitar! means, More! I think you wanted less silence and less bullshit, and I wanted to be surprised by what I said, and I wanted to really hear you. I was thinking of listening back to the tapes but it didn't feel right without you. Maybe we should listen to them together when we are old. I think the noise is only really important to me now because you are so far away.

I honestly can't remember what we talked about. I still have this feeling of freedom. This feeling of being in a risky place but not alone. Being on the outer edge of something by chance. When I look back at all the work I have done, all of everything, I feel most proud, again, not exactly the word, but most sure our method had some power beyond itself. It is not the method, not the noise, but the pushing back, the lack of explanation, the loss of utility, puncturing the flow of my own personal history. The way time had no purpose, no outcome and yet was not useless. The way our noise was the inverse of silence. And that inversion kept everything in balance making the rest of life porous to intentions again. Impose a word where it should not go VASTLY.

I was thinking of writing some notes so someone else could go through this process, what do you think? Good idea? So, what do you do? You begin by choosing someone. Just Vivian stirring.

Chloe, This detail, this habit,

Whatever rings true, take. But you will need to find someone because you cannot do this alone, although alone is a good place to start. Alone makes good beginnings. I was wondering what you think of us then. We have been on hold for two years. I am trying to work out if there was anything important about what we did. You thought we might have been sustaining a sort of negative space or perhaps drumming up courage for some decision. I wanted to really just stop reiterating myself and try to do something else with the only thing I am any good at, talking in a room with you.

Looking back, I wonder if you were a bit trapped or caught in the situation. It was my idea. I kept saying, If you want to change anything or suggest anything then go ahead. I kept giving you permission to make it what you wanted. I don't know if that really happened. Did you?

We were never rude to each other. I was a bit unkind at times. You found me frustrating, I know that. You would have preferred me to be smart when I was trying to just get along with you and find out if I could make you laugh. And, now I write this, I realise maybe that is why you told me jokes, maybe you wanted to make me laugh too. If anything, I have a sure sense of how our senses of humour were different, or are different. I think you are witty whereas my humour tends towards provocation. I am not sure if provocation is a sense of humour, maybe sometimes it made me laugh. Sometimes you laughed. Now, I really value that time, now I would love to have it back. While we were meeting I spoke to people in a different way, it had an impact on my social skills, which is totally down to you. I thought, if we can do this, then surely I can do this in the rest of my life. I discovered I could try but actually not everyone can listen to that kind of noise. I am not saying it was unique or specific to us but I do think we were unusual, in some regards. I think you wanted more silence and less bullshit and I wanted to be surprised by what I said and I wanted to really listen to you. I was thinking of listening back to the tapes but it didn't feel right without you. Maybe we should listen to them together tonight. I honestly can't remember what we talked about, I just have this feeling of freedom. I have this feeling of being unalone. Being on the outer edge of something but never alone. I dunno, I just wanted to say when I look back at everything, I feel most proud, again, not exactly the right word, most sure our noise had some power beyond us. It is not the noise but the pushing back, the lack of explanation, the loss of utility puncturing the flow of history. The way the time had no utility, no outcome and yet was not useless. The way we created the inverse of the rest of our lives. And that inverse, or inverted space, made life porous to intentions again. I was thinking of writing notes? Good idea? So, what do you do?

Aman, Choose someone,
That is what I did. Allowing for all the hidden intentions and motivations, I jumped. I did not spend much time considering who might want to do this with me. I have to say, and this will no doubt be shocking to you, but there will be others who won't work out. I began. I failed. I turned back to you.
Don't choose anyone who cannot be relied upon. They need to always, or almost always, turn up. Choose someone you do not know. You must have met this person but not have spoken to them in too much depth – an absolute stranger will not do. Think of someone who is not too convinced by themselves. A person with a sense of good folly who

is surprised they are perceived. You know who I mean? This is the right person to ask. Your curiosity struck me as vast and you seemed to know, mostly, you were being misinterpreted and that was that. But that was not you.

You will probably begin by thinking about your friends, take a step further, perhaps your friends' friends. Someone you cannot talk to. You never catch them, they never get you. If you have a good pattern with this person, then think again. I would recommend your brother's accountant, or your sister's ex-boyfriend. Wait. Someone you met a couple of times but who has gone now. We recorded our noise but really it is better if you don't. There are all those questions about what will happen to the recordings and who can, or cannot, listen. Someone you talked to. Listen if you can. Do not waste time on what the recording does to your noise, how it bends it a certain way and increases self-consciousness. All of this is just warming up. I sound like I don't want you to waste time, when actually the time wastes itself, stretching you out beyond purpose, so although the time is agreed, the duration is not. You can stop when you want, you can go on forever and you will think you know how much time has elapsed but you will be wrong – I was always wrong.

I realise I may have a structure: who, where, when

and snags, then endings. Although my experience has been there is no ending. There is no ending to each hour we spent together, I kept playing in my head after I left you, rehearsing what I might have said, we never paused. There was nothing for two years, and now we are thinking of beginning again.

I am not sure if it was one story told in instalments or many stories told one after another. Even though I cannot remember what we said, the whole I call a habit of conversation, a practice. And now, when I remember going to meet you, and then the whole two years, and the drift, they were as if I was in love. I was always excited because I had this practice, this habit, and the rest of my life seemed more vital, coloured by noise. I am in love now, very much in love, so I know it was like love. It was as good as love, and more, whatever it was has endured. More! means More!

Our habit was a horizon, so every repetition reminded me there was movement, potential, plasticity. Huh! Plasticity?

Peter, Resist the temptation to forge alliance,
I am not saying you can stop feeling what they feel. No, impossible. But this will not work if you try to take each other's sides. Avoid someone who offers a pattern. Avoid circles of affirmation. Think of someone you have noticed. They can be attractive

to you or not. It doesn't matter. Really, don't worry about it if you have wanted them now and again, once your habit gets underway you will realise physical attraction is quickly superseded.

I would say you need to find this person difficult, perhaps even childish, if they are beautiful in some strange way, all the better. Do you have them pictured now? I actually only had you in mind from the beginning but I doubted my choice and then started down a road at breakneck pace. As it turned out only you were able to commit to such a strange plan. Be intimidated by the oddity of the occasion. Be unsure about boundaries. You maybe thought you would be overwhelmed. You just didn't have the time, or couldn't explain to yourself why you might want to do this. I was prepared to travel to meet you and I think you could not understand why I would do that, why would I seek you out for this occasion with no aim, with no structure, with no outcome, with just this awkward, open, floating lake of uncertainty, Guitar!

Money is a mistake. The whole endeavour must work without money. And, any small exchanges, like buying the other person a crop of hay, tends to rattle the play. Later on, when you have been speaking for a year or so, it is no matter but at first we clung to this discussion, terrified of what might come up if we didn't talk about money. It is hard to stay at sea.

Shauna, Choose someone you eat with,

I was thinking, you are right, there is another way to have these conversations. You can use this method with the person you carefully forget. She is right, this has so much potential with someone you slumber with but never really talk to, it can work, perhaps miracles, in this scenario but I have never tested it so who can say. Something you can try. You are, after all, my spouse of sorts.

Do not change the place you meet, or the room you meet in. Unless you want a reset. We moved from an empty recording studio to a study carrel to empty Monday mornings at the public baths. Our heads were soundproofed. The recording studio smelled of coffee, the carrel of dust, the bath of chlorine. No booking in advance. The space must be for free. Why did we move? We were becoming friends. Move house again and again.

Maybe there is something to say about silence. Sitting together and there being lots of silence. How this could be good, then bad, changing direction swiftly. The silences were big and obvious. I had to find various ways of dealing with them. Of dealing with the feelings inside the silences – yours and mine – with no clear way out. Again, you need commitment. Stay with it. A lot like the moment before a question. STAY. Wait a little while. Put your feet up. I did. Do not rush in.

So, no switching rooms, unless you anticipate divorce. When you become frustrated, see it as a sign, something is about to give. And do not meet unless you are meeting for this. There is no other reason to meet. NONE. If you bump into each other in the street, if, then it is fine to pass without speaking. Guitar! Although that never happened to us, so I have no note to share.

How we did not bump into each other is strange as we were passing through the same rooms day and night. I imagined bumping into you. We did meet up once outside of the occasion, if you see what I mean, and it was a bad idea. Don't do that. We had an impersonal intimacy which, when given air in public, made every sentence travel along the wrong intonation, end with the wrong inflection, showed us up. I can say more but I need to sit a bit longer. There were immense silences. Silences we had learned to sustain, which in normal conversation would have left you standing outside alone.

Don't look too closely at your motivations. Don't see the person you choose as a motivation, the person is just your partner in the endeavour, not the reason. There will be no structure, your partner will try to make you into the structure, they will try to pursue your thoughts, why you chose them, why this place, why now, what do you want? If you don't know what you want you are in the perfect place to attempt to hear their noise. In a perfect place to unstructure the conversation. You are at an advantage.

I am advocating the lightest possible thinking be applied to these decisions, the decisions which make the occasion possible. The lightest touch possible. I know, it makes no sense, each note builds a pressure to somehow get the conditions of the occasion right, and yet I am also pressing for no thinking, no consideration, bad thoughtless decisions. Yes, both. You need to not think and yet be consistent, build a wall against overthinking and yet be meticulous.

Lesley, Choose someone kind,

Meet in a large institution, all these empty dishes have lots of unused space, and so many people passing through, your presence hardly matters. Their repetition makes any habit take hold. Intuition is structure, permits new meditations, takes the sting out of your neck.

I am going to suggest a few places you could meet. Each creates a different scene but all of them function well. Each has shortcomings and I will outline these as I go along. Maybe these places will no longer exist by the time you read this, but you can at least imagine the qualities to look for. Not a pub. A pub has the potential for the unstructuredness to be empty. Before I begin I want to just tell you the places you cannot practise, where it will not work.

You cannot practise in a home. Ideally, you should not be in a domestic setting of any kind. All the possibilities for flux are lost in any space where there are so many known objects, so many textures and colours chosen with care. The method is at a distance from care. The method requires a lot of care but is not a caring action, in an altruistic sense. And this raises questions about whether you need to know someone to care well. Care well always, have this anxious capacity for worry, for over-aid. Take the sting out carefully. Maybe the verb, 'present' is closer. Just concentrate on the method, on good practice. No, just practise.

You cannot practise at work. Unless your workplace is so big and alienating that nobody counts. You cannot practise in a cafe or where other people can comment. Privacy is the wrong word, but there is a sense of enclosure, in a park is fine, walking is perhaps too social. This method is not anti-social but contrary to any social script. In the snow, anywhere with discomfort can work. You could meet somewhere with a view, but the view itself will always dominate, maybe somewhere with a poor view, not dynamic, not hopeful, as in a railway station. Not a threshold. Not a place of arrival or departure. Somewhere still. Somewhere

quiet. Somewhere you will not be disturbed.
Somewhere without an illicit tone. People go to
places to be seen, this kind of place will not work.
This is not a date, this is not a meeting, this is not
a dance. You can try new places, sure you can try
under a desk, or a boardroom or an unpopular
waiting room, or a cupboard with a hidden window,
nowhere you look conspicuous, nowhere you want
to be for longer than an hour. No. Somewhere
warm. Ba! means the balloon might burst.

You could meet in a rural place, in a small town,
in a village, in a city I suppose. In this city there
are six study carrels with cinnamon swirl carpets,
empty bins and graffiti to make you blush. A cafe is
a poor alternative. Oh! and a recording booth. You
could borrow a space but then you would have to
tell someone why. Why you want to borrow their
garage, their spare room, their annex. So, the hardest
thing is finding the space.

I remember the main problem was not being
allowed to book the carrel, and not being allowed to
laugh. It is a study space after all. What is going on
in libraries? The care of people who have no home.

Go to the fourth floor of the Mitchell Library,
pay at the reception. Go to number 6. If somebody
is in then go to number 1, if it is busy try number
4. They cost £6 an hour. You will need your library
pass. You will need to arrive early. At first you will

talk about the Librarian after she tells you to stop making so much noise. Then you won't want to look at each other.

Should you talk about the conversation? No. Any point? NO. I am writing these notes so you don't have to talk about anything. So you can enjoy the noise, of each other, of your habit. Nobody can help, only practise, only the practice of unstructuring week after week can prepare you for the difficulty and, suddenly, you begin to handle the consequences. Feeling the consequences and the implications of the consequences. Most of the practice happens in the six soft days when you will struggle not to think of the next occasion. The not preparing, the not knowing how to not prepare is one of the various skills learned, a skill you need. A technique of not thinking, not structuring, not wondering, not collapsing the possibilities in the soft days. When the hard day appears, the not thinking becomes a meditation, on what? A meditation on suspending all forward thinking. You will catch yourself catching your thoughts drifting towards, I wonder if she will turn up? I wonder how he is? I wonder – stop it. Just STOP. If you think you may love this person, you will consider what to wear, how you may want to appear? That love is just a shell. Your vanity will be undone by this method.

It will be your idea, this noise, so you will be

responsible. For keeping the time. For the edges of the time, for the care of the other person too, for attending to their nervous feelings, for never taking anything, for never presuming, for never assuming they are on your side, you are both there to see what happens. Just go right along. *You'll* start happening too. If you want to unstructure time, you must keep the time. The time is not yours or theirs, it belongs to the habit, it is a condition to be maintained. No slips, no errors. There will be errors and you will feel how, after you stop making noise, any further word beyond the hour, any slight overflow will build complicity and seem awkward, more awkward than the longest silence. Don't say anything. I think we said a few things, casual chat, as if we were allowed, as if no one was listening and it felt fake. As if we were manufacturing something, when inside the room, inside the method, we felt free, unselfconscious, without limits.

What is the method? You find a room. You find a person. The person must be reliable. You set a time. Every week you meet this person outside the room. You go into the room together, close the door and after an hour you stop. You leave the room, close the door. It doesn't matter how many weeks go by, you both continue until one of you stops.

Once, only once, I sat in the room alone. I sat and missed you.

I missed it.

I minded the method.

You might find you need this method. I didn't really need the method, I thought I did at the time. I had been in the same city for two decades. You might need to leave but you cannot go. And so I will show you another good game that I know. You make an escape attempt. This will seem like a necessity, not a choice. There will be no choice, this or nothing. Guitar! means, Bye-bye! How do you break out of a cycle of wanting intimacy but constantly facing your own schemes and traps? Guitar! means, Hold me! Your own vanity keeps rising up whenever you try to just speak honestly to someone, to just simply. Guitar! means, Carry me! When talking and listening, there are always your petty concerns in the way, literally filling up the conversation with intent. Always overthinking, always rehearsing, always strategising, always scheming how to make yourself look better to this person. You might need the method then.

Isobel, Choose someone quiet,

All your investments may be devalued, you stop and ask, How can I get out of this? How can I call it off? What do I have to do? I need the method now. I need it but it is almost impossible for me to go back. I need to start speaking to him again. I know

I could use the method now, really use it. Rather than try it out or play with it or observe its effects, comment on it. Be NOT a commentator. Make lots of noise. Noise has no angles. I think he is too busy now. I doubt he would go back. Maybe he needs the method too. I doubt it. I think he is happy. This method is not only for periods of unhappiness, but for times when you want to run away and find yourself weighed down with sincerity. Guitar! means, Carry me please!

Ba! live. Or expire.

Not only does the method unstructure time within the time set aside for practice (you could say the noise nest) but time outside the occasion, outside the praxis, starts to unravel. The premise and the practice have an affect which is gently elastic, you start to notice things, you start to sense how certain people are extruding or shrinking time. And, at first, this seems like a hiccup but then it becomes acute. By engaging with certain people or avoiding others, by choosing, sounds start to resonate or vanish as they hit the bottom of the guitar.

This is not life changing, and by that I mean I did not want to change my life. I was able to live differently, maybe that is changing your life? I do not know, but you will find there are few experiences which are not felt in a part of you that is more aware of limits, the limits of each occasion. Each interaction is felt.

Choose each other,

It doesn't matter if the person you practise with is nervous. You will be nervous too. The outer shell of the practice is illicit, some of the conditions could be misinterpreted. There are no rules to say you cannot fall in love or be seduced but if you are here reading this I imagine you are seeking a habit with a purchase, a play, a grip beyond grappling with a body. I mean, grappling is great, it is fine to have whatever motivation you have. I just want to warn you there is a tension present, but this tension creates concentration. Gaze at each other for a long, long time.

Giulia, Choose someone,

You are so smart, do not try. I am trying to imagine who will need this method. Out of all the things I have done in my life, this one process seems to be the most useful, the one thing worth telling you about. I don't assume.

I forgot to say, keep yourself safe, don't meet anyone you cannot trust. Trust is central to the habit. Not only to your safety but to noise itself. If this person only wants to question your choice, to criticise and complain, then practice is impossible. You will stop. You might stop and start several times. It might take a while to find someone. Intuition is the best guide. Use your intuition. Be safe, be sure this person is serious. There are other people like you who want nothing but this.

This is not something to do when you are in love, you will never find the time if you are in love. This is not something to do if you are very unhappy, the conversation is very unhelpful, unpractical and often frustrating. You can be very busy and still have time for noise. You just need to be going along with your life. Not too sad nor too happy, just going along. Sometimes it is good to think about why you have put your life in a certain order. Or why particular people are around you? Why are you involved? When you are older I want you to know these things. Guitar? is a serious question. Is there blossom on the pum-tree?

Vivian, Go your own way,

I don't know how you found these notes, this drill. What kind of search would lead you here? What will you say? I emptied your house, your bookshelves, there it was. I don't know. Joy will lead you here. Or that certain feeling of not being able to speak fully. Not being able to get to the end. Right at the end of what you want to say is that moment of not knowing, of having reached some edge, after that you have no choice but to listen. Close your mouth and wait for the next, for the nest, for the nope. Always go back to your Guitar!

Allow your life to be shaped by the people you are loving. Let your love of people bring a structure. You will have concerns for people you do not know, you can allow those people to shape your time too. You will sometimes need, to pause. The rhythm of loving people will sometimes take over and then you might think, this is just a pattern, somebody spoke to me and I did not recognise myself. Guitar! means suitcase. Guitar! means spark. Voices. Instructions. Guitar! is the hope that a guitar will turn up in this story.

This thing I did, is not really so important, I think you will find it yourself, on your own, without any directions. No need to read on unless you miss my voice and you want to listen to me for a while longer. I could talk about other things but this one thing might come in useful. These notes are for you but do not follow them. Do not follow me. These notes show you what can be done. Listen out for your own cues. Don't wait, keep stepping forward, trust the ringing, you will always be right.

Let's begin. Guitar! means, Hello! This is how you learn to speak.

And now? I wish I could talk to you. I miss our noise. I didn't look at you once when we spoke, if I looked straight at you I thought you might go, vanish or withdraw. I wish I had not tried to charm you. I just wanted you to STAY. If you were here, I would say something like, My hands are always cold, and then wait. You, somewhere else, another place entirely, you would speak slowly as if after a long journey. Your thoughts were very much your own, I liked meeting them, always totally outside the room, always strange, but always clear sounds coming back. I miss you. You are too far away now. Is it possible to start again? I am not sure if I can ask you, if you said no there is no way back.

This is it! There was a symmetry, fabricated at first but then momentum! One method out of many possibilities. Each person who tries will find their own. I tried to surprise myself. Did you? Once I get out from under you there is no way back.

I think we complained but we did not moan. We didn't take anything into the room. Step inside without a care. Step inside without care. Careless. Step lightly. I cared to continue. I stopped because... I cannot remember.

You are too much my equal and that is a true measurement, equivocal and permanent. I am trying to write this method down. I keep stopping and starting. It is nothing, right? It is almost nothing.

But not quite, there is a pitch and a determination to be strangers, and a way of doing all this, I need to write to Francis. Oh and Chloe.

Choose anyone,

The room is still there. The recording booth is still there with its total silence behind the heavy door. Someone has left a ballpoint pen without a lid, there is an A4 sheet of paper weathering neglect, gathering, what?

What goes on inside? You will know how to answer, whatever is said you will know what to say, but do not say this. Do not say the thing you know how to say. Do not say the thing which would bring most comfort, do not say the thing which would give him an idea of what to say next. Do not. Just stop. Wait. Do not think of something witty and say that. Do not think. STOP. Do not try for a non-sequitur. Do not make a sentence about the silence. Do not express your reservations about what you were going to say before you changed your mind. Do not comment on your inner thoughts, do not comment on what you believe to be their inner thoughts. You are thinking if I do not say these things there is nothing left, that is not true. Do not observe the weather, or the room you are sitting in, just don't do all those easy things, you will lose yourself.

No need to read on unless you miss my noise and want to listen to me for a while longer.

You will live for a long time.

Acknowledgements and thanks

Page 131, paraphrased from 'Sank it deep in the cake.'
The Cat in the Hat, Dr Seuss, (HarperCollins, London, 1985)

Page 146, 'Just go right along. *You'll* start happening too.'
Oh, the Places You'll Go! Dr Seuss, (HarperCollins, London, 2016)

Original version of pages 7–9 published in *Terra Cotta,* Emily Speed, 2019.

Thank you Francis McKee for the photographs.

Thank you Jane Rolo.

Thank you Peter Amoore, Kitty Anderson, Alice Bain, Simon Buckley, Giulia Lazzaro, Lin Li, Chin Li, Shauna McMullen, Chloe Reid, Aman Sandhu, Isobel Lutz-Smith, Lesley Young, George Ziffo.

Thank you to Dan Brown, Debi Banerjee and Edinburgh Sculpture Workshop.

Guitar!
Sarah Tripp

Cover artwork by Ciara Phillips
Designed by Jana Parvee
Edited by Lizzie Homersham
Proofread by Miranda Blennerhassett

Published by Book Works, London
Distributed by Book Works (UK)
and Idea Books (rest of world)

ISBN 978 1 906012 83 0

Book Works receives National Portfolio funding from Arts
Council England. This publication is generously supported
by Creative Scotland and The Glasgow School of Art.

Book Works
19 Holywell Row
London EC2A 4JB
www.bookworks.org.uk
Tel. +44 (0)20 7247 2203